who knew?

Beauty
Wonders

Simple Secrets
and Homemade
Recipes for a
Glamorous
New You

Bruce Lubin & Jeanne Bossolina-Lubin

Cover design by Michele L. Trombley

ISBN: 978-0-9883264-4-6

Printed and bound in the United States of America

2 4 6 8 10 9 7 5 4 3 1

Please visit us online at www.WhoKnewTips.com

TABLE OF CONTENTS

Chapter 1:
Put Your Best Face Forward: Facial Cleansers,
Toners, and Masks
4

Chapter 2:
Hair-Brained: Smart Tips and Tricks for Lovely Locks
21

Chapter 3:
The Skin You Live In: Natural Recipes and
Tips for Healthier Skin
34

Chapter 4:
Going to Extremes: Pampering Your Hands and Feet
50

Chapter 5:
Baths, Butters, Lotions, and More
64

CHAPTER 1

Put Your Best Face Forward: Cleansers, Toners, and Masks

Puffy eyes, pimples, blackheads, and wrinkles—we've experienced them all and lived to tell about it. To keep you looking your best, we've assembled these simple yet effective homemade facial cleansers, scrubs, toners, masks, and lip balms. Using fresh fruits, herbs, and vegetables, you'll tackle your oily skin, age spots, and dry skin—or, if you're one of the lucky ones, you'll keep your normal skin in great shape.

Pumpkin Facial

1 can pumpkin puree (not the pumpkin pie variety!)
¼ cup plain yogurt
¼ cup honey
¼ ground almonds
olive oil

For clean, soft skin—and a clever way to use up that can of pumpkin that's been gathering dust in your pantry since Thanksgiving—try this facial mask. Mix together the canned pumpkin with the yogurt, honey, ground almonds, and a drizzle of olive oil. Apply to skin, and take a hot bath to let the steam and enzymes in the mask do their work. After 10 minutes, rinse and apply your normal moisturizer. Refrigerate any leftovers and use within a week.

Kiwi Clean

1 kiwifruit
2 tablespoons plain yogurt
1 tablespoon honey
1 tablespoon olive oil (or almond oil)
1 teaspoon cornmeal
orange water (optional)

Here's an all-natural facial cleanser that works well for normal-to-dry skin types. Puree a peeled kiwifruit with the yogurt, honey, olive or almond oil, and cornmeal. Add a splash of orange water. Rub gently into face and neck, then rinse well.

Gone Bananas

1 ripe banana
honey
1 teaspoon lemon juice

In need of a soothing, calming facial mask at the end of a long day? Mash a ripe banana in a bowl with a drizzle of honey, and add the lemon juice to stop the mixture from browning. Apply to your face, and leave on for 15 minutes. Rinse with a warm washcloth. This mask is especially good for acne-prone skin because of the toning properties of lemon. Just be sure to apply moisturizer with sunscreen, since your skin may be a bit more sensitive due to the lemon juice. Now, aren't you glad we said banana?

Want to give your lips a boost? Rub them with cinnamon! Cinnamon increases blood flow, giving your lips a fuller look. Rinse, and then apply your lipstick as usual.

Thyme for Toner

2 sprigs fresh thyme (or 1½ teaspoons dried)
2 teaspoons fennel seeds
½ cup boiling water
1 tablespoon freshly squeezed lemon juice

It's long been known that fennel seeds can reduce puffiness and skin irritation, and that thyme has antiseptic and astringent properties. Here's how to use both to make a gentle facial toner. Strip the leaves from the sprigs of fresh thyme. Crush the fennel seeds in a mortar and pestle. Place both herbs in a bowl with the boiling water and lemon juice. Cover, and allow the mixture to steep for 20 minutes. Strain the toner into a jar, and store in the refrigerator for up to two weeks. Apply the cool mixture with cotton balls to clean skin to soothe redness and tighten pores.

Honey and Oats Delight

½ cup instant or rolled oats
1 tablespoon honey
1 tablespoon vinegar
1 tablespoon ground almonds

Here's another great oatmeal scrub that's perfect for normal skin. Blend together the oats, honey, vinegar, and ground almonds. If the mixture is too dry, add a drop or two of water to make a thick paste. Apply to clean skin and leave for 10–15 minutes or until dry. Rinse with warm water for revitalized skin.

❋ BONUS BEAUTY TIP ❋

Fear you're getting a pimple? Dab the offending spot with a little tea tree oil, then cover it with a bit of toothpaste. The tea tree oil is an antiseptic, and the toothpaste has an anti-inflammatory effect.

Lavender Facial Scrub

1½ cups rolled oats
¾ cup almonds
1 tablespoon dried lavender
¾ cup honey
1¼ cups white kaolin clay

If you have oily skin, try this sweetly scented scrub. Pulse together the oats, almonds, and dried lavender in a blender. Mix in the honey and white kaolin clay. (You can find the clay online or at stores that carry natural beauty products.) Remove a tablespoon of the scrub and mix with water to make a thick paste. Massage over face and neck, and leave on for 10–15 minutes. The clay will help remove impurities and excess oil, while the oats and almonds will exfoliate and soothe skin. As a bonus, lavender is great for stress relief! Store the leftovers in the refrigerator in a closed container. It should last for three weeks.

Butter(Milk) Me Up

1 tablespoon rolled or instant oats
1 tablespoon honey
¼ cup buttermilk

This mask contains two exfoliating powerhouses—oatmeal and buttermilk. Buttermilk contains lactic acid, which helps dissolve dead skin cells to reveal younger-looking skin. Puree the oats, honey, and milk in a blender. Massage gently into the face, and leave on for 10–15 minutes. Rinse with lukewarm water.

Cucumber Eye Pads

½ cucumber, peeled
¼ cup cold water

Here's a unique twist on the traditional cucumber-slices-on-eyes trick. Chop the cucumber and puree it in a blender with the water, then strain the mixture into a spray bottle. Spritz the cooling mixture onto round cosmetic pads to saturate, and place them on your eyes. Do this anytime you have some extra redness or puffiness around the eyes. For us, that's almost a daily occurrence! Store the leftovers in the refrigerator for a week or so.

Cool as a Cucumber

1 cucumber
½ cup yogurt

You put cucumber slices on tired, puffy eyes, so why not on your whole face? Try this nourishing mix to tighten pores, reduce puffiness, and tone skin. Grate the cucumber on the side of a box grater or in the food processor. Mix in the ½ cup yogurt or enough to bind the mixture together. Apply the cooling blend to clean skin, and leave it on for five minutes. Rinse with cool water.

❋ BONUS BEAUTY TIP ❋

Lipstick can serve double-duty as a cream blush. Just dab a little on your cheeks and blend. This is also a great tip for an evening out when you're carrying a tiny clutch that barely has enough room for your keys and cell phone.

Say Yes to Carrots

1 carrot, sliced
2 tablespoons honey
¼ cup plain yogurt

Carrots are rich in beta-carotene, a natural form of vitamin A, and they have antioxidant properties. Try this creamy facial mask to take advantage of their benefits. Boil the carrot slices until tender. Add them to a blender, and puree with the honey and yogurt. Spread the mixture on your face, and leave it on for 10 minutes. Rinse with a warm washcloth, then moisturize as usual.

Green Monster

1 ripe avocado
1 carrot, boiled until tender
½ cup heavy cream
3 tablespoons honey

It used to be said that avocados were a "poor man's butter," but their health benefits could not be richer. They're packed with vitamin E and antioxidants, and they have an anti-inflammatory effect. Carrots are filled with beta-carotene. This creamy facial helps to rebuild skin collagen and improve texture. In a small bowl, mash together the avocado and carrot. Slowly stir in the heavy cream and honey. Apply to your face, and leave on for 10–15 minutes. Rinse with lukewarm water.

An Un-matcha-ble Mask

1 tablespoon matcha (green tea powder)
½ ripe avocado
2 tablespoons avocado oil

This anti-inflammatory facial mask offers a one-two punch with the antioxidant power of green tea and avocado. Matcha is a powdery Japanese green tea that

comes in a small tin. You can find it at health food and specialty stores. (It's what gives green tea ice cream its flavor and color.) Mash the avocado together with the green tea powder and oil. Apply the rich mixture to the skin, and leave on for 10–15 minutes. Rinse with lukewarm water, and enjoy your younger-looking skin.

❋ BONUS BEAUTY TIP ❋

To exfoliate skin in a hurry, apply any of these all-natural ingredients directly to the face with a cotton ball: milk, pineapple juice, tomato juice, or orange juice.

The Eyes Have It

2 bags chamomile tea

The same chamomile tea that calms an upset stomach can also ease puffy, irritated eyes. Soak tea bags in cold water for a few minutes until they are plump. Squeeze out a bit of excess water and then place the bags on closed eyes for several minutes. Alternatively, you can use chilled chamomile tea as a refreshing facial spritzer.

Tea Treats Oil

3 bags chamomile tea
2–3 cups water

If you have oily, clogged pores, try this steamy facial. Boil the water, and add the tea bags. Cover, and let the bags steep for about 10 minutes. Place your face over the open pot, and cover your head with a towel to allow the rising steam to open and unclog your pores. After about 10 minutes, rinse your face with cold water. As a bonus, chamomile is also a great stress reliever!

A Sticky Solution

¼ cup honey
1–2 tablespoons milk

Here's an easy, inexpensive way to moisturize your skin and help prevent wrinkles. Mix together the honey and milk. Spread the mixture on your face, and leave for 10 minutes. Rinse well with warm water.

❋ BONUS BEAUTY TIP ❋

Long-lasting lipsticks are great, but they can be a pain to remove at the end of the day. Try putting a little olive or vegetable oil on a cotton ball to wipe the color away.

Minty Fresh

1 tablespoon brown sugar
1 tablespoon regular sugar
sweet almond oil (or vitamin E oil)
peppermint essential oil

Nothing's worse than chapped lips in winter. Here's a minty scrub that tackles the problem at the source— and smells fantastic. In a small bowl, stir together the two sugars, and start drizzling in the sweet almond or vitamin E oil until the mixture is a little runny. Add a few drops of peppermint essential oil and stir well. To use, take a small amount and rub gently on your lips for 30 seconds. Rinse and apply lip balm as usual. Store the excess in a jar in the refrigerator for whenever you need a little extra pampering.

The Goodness of Grapes

5 red grapes
2–3 teaspoons olive (or grape-seed) oil
1 tablespoon honey

For a few years, we've been hearing about the benefits of resveratrol, the powerful antioxidant in red grapes and red wine. It helps boost the production of collagen, giving your skin a younger look. Try this mask to help minimize fine lines and firm the skin. Combine the grapes, oil, and honey in a blender. Apply the mask to the face, and leave for 10–15 minutes. Rinse with warm water.

❋ BONUS BEAUTY TIP ❋

If you have an eyeliner pencil that keeps crumbling when you try to use it, stick it in the freezer for 20 minutes to firm it up.

Plump Up the Volume

3 tablespoons beeswax
1 tablespoon vegetable oil
1 teaspoon ginger, grated

For lips worthy of Angelina Jolie, try this plumping balm. Melt the beeswax and vegetable oil in a double boiler.

Using a rasp grater, grate a teaspoon of ginger onto a piece of cheesecloth. Squeeze the cheesecloth over the wax mixture to release some of the fragrant ginger juices, and stir to combine. Keep the balm in a small jar, and spread a little on your lips anytime you want a little extra boost!

Crazy for Cranberry

1 tablespoon avocado oil (or sweet almond oil)
10 fresh cranberries
1 teaspoon honey
1 drop vitamin E oil (from a capsule)

For a seasonal solution to chapped winter lips—and a great DIY gift idea for the holidays—try this cranberry lip balm! In a microwave-safe bowl, mix together all of the above ingredients. Microwave on high until the mixture begins to boil. Remove carefully as the bowl may be hot. Mash the berries with a fork and stir well to combine. After the mixture has cooled for 10 minutes, strain it into a small portable tin, making sure to remove all of the fruit pieces. Cool completely, and smile because you've made your own great-smelling lip balm!

Be Gone, Blackheads!

1 egg white

Why spend your money on expensive blackhead-removal strips when you can make this easy-as-pie version at home? This single-ingredient mask has the added bonus of helping tighten pores, control unwanted oiliness, and brighten skin. Whisk together an egg white for a minute or so. Then brush the mixture on your face and neck, avoiding the eyes and mouth. Place tissues against your face, making holes for your eyes, nose, and mouth. Allow the egg white to dry completely before peeling the tissues off. Wash with lukewarm water and moisturize as usual. For particularly oily skin, repeat twice a week.

❋ BONUS BEAUTY TIP ❋

If you want a quick pore cleanser, look no further than the white Elmer's Glue in your child's craft box. Spread a thin layer on the problem area (avoiding the eyes), let dry, and peel away. It works on blackheads, and it's so much fun that you'll feel like a kid again!

Lentil Loofah

1 cup red lentils (masoor dal)
¼–½ cup coconut water
¼ cup dried orange peel (optional)

Here's a unique scrub with excellent exfoliating properties. Soak the lentils overnight in the coconut water. There should be enough liquid to moisten all of the lentils, but they should not be drenched. In the morning, pulse this mixture in a food processor with the optional orange peel until you have a coarse, damp scrub. To use, scoop out a tablespoon or two of the scrub and add water to moisten. Massage over face and neck to remove dead skin cells. Rinse with cool water to reveal silky smooth skin. You can also use this as an allover body scrub. Store leftovers in an airtight jar in the refrigerator. It should keep for 2–3 weeks.

Out, Darn Spots!

1 teaspoon lemon juice
1 teaspoon honey
2 teaspoons plain yogurt

Do you have acne scars or other dark spots on your face? You can use the enzymes in certain foods to help lighten them! Here's a soothing mask to try. Stir together the lemon juice, honey, and yogurt in a small bowl. Apply to your face, and leave on for about 10 minutes. Rinse with warm water.

Fresh Parsley and Sour Cream Mask

¼ cup sour cream
2 teaspoons finely chopped parsley

Here's a gentle mask for lightening dark spots that sounds more like a dip for chips! Mix together the sour cream and parsley in a small bowl, and apply to clean skin. Leave for about 15 minutes, and rinse with cool water.

❋ BONUS BEAUTY TIP ❋

Sipping a nonfat venti latte at Starbucks? Grab a few napkins to go. Beauty insiders consider them incredible face blotting sheets.

CHAPTER 2

Hair-Brained: Smart Tips and Tricks for Lovely Locks

Hair can be so fickle. In icy January, it's flat and dull, and then during an August heat wave, it's frizzy and unmanageable. Also, there are the year-round problems of oiliness, dryness, dandruff, and thinning hair. In this chapter, you'll find a whole range of do-it-yourself shampoos, conditioners, masks, and scalp toners, along with tricks to boost volume and shine and repair damaged hair. So grab that can of coconut milk and an avocado, and we'll help you make every day (or most of them, anyway!) a good-hair day.

Tropical Therapy for Tresses

1 tablespoon coconut oil
1 vitamin E capsule
1½ teaspoons lemon juice (for light-colored hair)
rosemary essential oil (for dark-colored hair)

Is your hair in need of deep conditioning? Here's a simple hair mask that has the added benefit of brightening. Place the coconut oil in a microwave-safe bowl, and microwave on low, just until it starts to liquefy. Remove and add the contents of the vitamin E capsule (you can puncture it with a pin). If you have light-colored hair, stir in the lemon juice. For dark-colored hair, add a few drops of rosemary essential oil instead. Massage into damp hair, and cover with a towel or shower cap for 15–20 minutes, then wash and condition as usual.

Banana Blend

1 banana, peeled
1 cup cantaloupe, chopped
1 tablespoon grape-seed oil
1 tablespoon plain yogurt

Puree all of the ingredients in the blender. Apply to clean, damp hair and leave on for 30 minutes. Rinse with lukewarm water to reveal soft, sleek hair!

Holy Guacamole!

1 ripe avocado
3 tablespoons olive oil

Avocado is not just healthy for your body, it's also a great moisturizer for the hair. Mash together a ripe avocado with the olive oil. Work the mask through damp hair, and cover with a shower cap or plastic wrap for 20–30 minutes. Rinse and shampoo as usual for soft, manageable hair.

❋ BONUS BEAUTY TIP ❋

Brush your hair before you wash it. By doing so, you'll evenly distribute the natural oils in the hair, thus reducing breakage.

An Egg-Cellent Shampoo

2 eggs
2 teaspoons freshly squeezed lemon juice
2 teaspoons olive or grape-seed oil
2 teaspoons mayonnaise

Hate that winter scalp itchiest? This soothing egg and lemon shampoo will moisturize and soothe hair and scalp alike. Whisk the eggs together in a small bowl, then stir in the lemon juice, oil, and mayonnaise. Use in place of your regular shampoo, and condition as usual.

❋ BONUS BEAUTY TIP ❋

You know we can never find enough uses for baking soda! Here's another great one. The next time you wash your hair, add a teaspoon of baking soda to your hand along with the shampoo. Wash as usual, and get ready for super bouncy hair.

DIY Dry Shampoo

1–2 tablespoons cornstarch

Lately, we've noticed a booming new trend in hair-care products: dry shampoo. The idea is that this product can be used to revitalize less-than-fresh locks when you don't have time to wash your hair. But why spend anywhere from $3 to $15 on dry shampoo when you've already got the perfect substitute in your pantry? It's cornstarch. Granted, this tip is a little messy, so stand on a towel, or apply in the shower before turning on the water. Sprinkle the cornstarch on dry hair and massage throughout the hair and scalp. Leave for five minutes to allow it to absorb excess oil, and then brush it out. Instantly revitalized hair!

Coconut Shampoo

½ cup coconut milk
⅔ cup liquid castile soap (such as Dr. Bronner's)
2 teaspoons apricot kernel oil
5 drops coconut essential oil

This rich shampoo is great for African-American hair, and it smells like you're on vacation! Pour all of the ingredients into a bottle, seal, and shake to combine. To apply, wet hair, and lather in the shampoo. Rinse, and follow with your favorite conditioner. You may need to shake before using each time.

❋ BONUS BEAUTY TIP ❋

We don't want to sound like your mother, but you are what you eat. A healthy diet can help create stronger, more lustrous hair.

Dandruff Dressing

2 tablespoons olive oil
2 tablespoons cider vinegar

Ok, we admit it: This rinse sounds like salad dressing, but it works on dandruff! Whisk together the oil and vinegar, and massage into the scalp for a few minutes. The

olive oil helps loosen the dandruff (and moisturize the scalp) and the vinegar removes the flakes. You can also try this with straight cider vinegar.

Winter Wonder

½ cup honey
olive oil (2 tablespoons for normal to oily hair; 4 tablespoons for dry, damaged hair)
4 drops rosemary essential oil

All winter long, we shuttle back and forth between dry, overheated offices and freezing cold streets. It's no wonder our hair starts to resemble straw! This terrific hair mask combines the shine-boosting powers of honey with the hydrating properties of olive oil. First, warm the oil gently in a saucepan. Whisk in the honey and essential oil. Apply to clean, damp hair; cover, then allow to condition for 30 minutes. Rinse and shampoo as usual. Winter flyaways, be gone!

✽ BONUS BEAUTY TIP ✽

To make sure your conditioner penetrates all of your hair evenly, comb your hair thoroughly after you've applied it.

For Deep Healing

½ cup honey
½ cup coconut milk
1 tablespoon coconut oil

Here's another intensive treatment for dry hair. In small saucepan, gently heat the honey, coconut milk, and coconut oil, stirring to combine. You want the mixture to be warm, but not hot enough to burn you. Remove from the heat. Massage into damp hair, and cover with a shower cap. The heat will help open the hair shaft, allowing the moisturizers to penetrate more fully. Leave for 30 minutes, then rinse. Repeat once a week.

Brittle Hair Booster

2 tablespoons chickpea (garbanzo) flour
1 cup coconut milk

Here's another great use for coconut milk: to strengthen brittle hair. In a small bowl, mix together the coconut milk with the chickpea flour. (Chickpea flour is available in health-food stores and Indian grocery stores.) Rub the mixture into the hair and scalp. Wait 10 minutes, then rinse.

❋ BONUS BEAUTY TIP ❋

Flatirons have become an indispensable part of many women's beauty routines. To reduce hair damage, try switching to a silicone version. It's faster, which means less time that your hair is in contact with those hot plates.

Summer Saver

½ cucumber, peeled and chopped
1 egg
1 tablespoon olive oil

If you swim on a regular basis, you know the havoc that chlorine can wreak on your hair. This treatment can help counteract some of the damage caused by those laps in the pool. Puree the cucumber, egg, and oil in a blender until smooth. Apply to wet hair, and leave on for 10–15 minutes. Rinse with cool water, and repeat whenever your hair is a little fried!

Put the Lime in the Coconut

1 14-ounce can coconut milk
2 limes
cornstarch

Here's a great tip for African-American women looking for a natural alternative to those chemical-laden relaxers. In a small bowl, juice the limes and stir the juice into the coconut milk. Transfer the mixture to a small saucepan on medium heat. Start whisking in a few tablespoons of cornstarch, stirring constantly until the mixture starts to thicken. When it reaches the desired consistency, remove it from the heat and let cool slightly. Massage thoroughly through the hair, then cover it with a shower cap or plastic wrap. After 45–60 minutes, you can rinse it out.

Moisturizing Mayonnaise Mask

3–4 tablespoons mayonnaise

For a simple hair mask, apply mayonnaise directly to damp hair, cover, and wait 30 minutes. Shampoo and condition as usual.

❋ BONUS BEAUTY TIP ❋

Need a quick way to tame flyaways? Take a drop or two of grape-seed or olive oil, rub between your hands, and apply to dry hair, paying special attention to the ends.

Rehydrate with Hot Oil

¼ cup olive, coconut, grape-seed, or almond oil

There's no need to buy commercial hot oil treatments when you can use oils you've already got at home. Gently heat the oil in a saucepan until it's warm. Be careful: You don't want it so hot that it will burn your skin. Massage into damp hair, and cover with plastic wrap for 20 minutes before shampooing.

Body Building

3 tablespoons Epsom salts
3 tablespoons conditioner

Give fine or thinning hair a volume boost with Epsom salts. In a microwave-safe bowl, stir together the Epsom salts and conditioner. Microwave on 50 percent power until warm. Apply the mixture to clean, damp hair, and leave for 20 minutes. Rinse and style as usual.

Flat Fixer

¼ cup rice
1 cup warm water

If your hair is looking limp, try this unique trick. Allow the rice to soak overnight in the warm water. In the morning, strain off the liquid into a spray bottle, and spritz it on damp hair. The starch will cling to each strand, creating lots of body and volume.

❋ BONUS BEAUTY TIP ❋

If you wear a ponytail regularly, try to change it up! Wearing a ponytail in the same spot all of the time can cause your hairline to shift in a particular direction.

Herbal Scalp Toner

Fresh rosemary sprigs
Fresh sage leaves

If you have an oily scalp, try this toning rinse. Rosemary and sage are great astringents that also help stimulate hair follicles. Take sprig or two of rosemary, along with equal parts sage, and place the herbs in a small saucepan with water to cover. Bring to a simmer and remove from the heat. Allow to steep for 10–20 minutes, then

strain. Massage into wet hair daily. Store the leftovers in the refrigerator for up to two weeks.

Growth Spurt

5 drops lavender essential oil
5 drops bay essential oil
3 tablespoons almond or grape-seed oil

Looking for a natural solution to thinning hair? Here's a terrific scalp massage that stimulates blood flow in the hair follicles and may spur hair growth. Mix the essential oils into the almond or grape-seed oil. Massage a small amount into the scalp every day, and leave for 15–20 minutes before rinsing out.

For an Even Dye Job

2 tablespoons baking soda
2 cups water

If you're dyeing your hair at home, you should know that the chemicals in hair dye can soak in faster in lighter sections of your hair, creating an uneven look. Avoid that problem with—what else?—baking soda. Dissolve the baking soda in the water, and rinse your hair with it before applying the dye. The baking soda will lift the cuticle, which will allow the dye to penetrate evenly and create a more professional look.

❋ BONUS BEAUTY TIP ❋

To preserve that great dye job you just got at the salon, rinse your hair regularly with white vinegar to seal the hair cuticle.

End Split Ends

1 egg yolk
2 tablespoons olive or grape-seed oil
2 teaspoons honey

Sometimes our schedule is so busy that it's hard even to make time for a haircut. Here's how we temporarily smooth split ends. Mix together the yolk, oil, and honey. Apply the mixture to damp hair, cover with a shower cap, and leave for 30 minutes. Shampoo as usual. The emollient properties in the ingredients will seal the ends for a few days until you can get yourself in your stylist's chair for a proper trim.

Papaya Power

½ papaya
½ cup plain yogurt

If you're looking to strengthen your hair, look no further than the papaya. Mash the flesh of half a papaya with the yogurt. Apply to damp hair, and cover with a shower cap for 20 minutes. Rinse, and wash and condition as usual.

CHAPTER 3

The Skin You Live In: Natural Recipes and Tips for Healthier Skin

The skin is the body's largest organ, so it's important to give it the care it deserves. In this chapter, we give you recipes and tips for coping with oily, dry, and flaky skin. You'll also learn how to treat cellulite, inflammation, unwanted hair, spots, blotches, and more. Want to boost circulation and remove dead skin cells? Check out the ginger-sugar scrub. Is your skin red and inflamed in winter? Try the simple yogurt-turmeric body mask. Feeling

rough around the elbows? The solution is simple, and only requires a little salt and lime.

Cellulite Solution

¼ cup ground coffee
2 tablespoons sugar
2 tablespoons honey
2 tablespoons olive oil

If you're looking for a quick way to reduce the appearance of cellulite, try coffee! When rubbed against the skin, it helps to increase circulation and make the cellulite less noticeable. Mix together all of the ingredients in a small bowl. You should have a damp paste. Massage over problem areas like your thighs, using a circular motion. Rinse to reveal firmer-looking skin!

Smooth Out the Rough Patches

¼ cup sea salt
2 tablespoons apricot kernel oil
5 drops apricot essential oil

Here's a great apricot–sea salt body scrub for smoothing out rough spots on elbows, hands, feet, or wherever you need a little extra help. Mix together all of the ingredients, then rub onto the skin. Rinse with warm water.

You've probably heard it before, but wondered if it was true: Does Preparation H really diminish fine lines and wrinkles? It does! Try applying a small amount to an inconspicuous area, to see if it irritates your skin.

Kiwi Power

2 kiwis, peeled and chopped
¼ cup cornmeal

Kiwis are rich in vitamin C, which is known for its potential as an anti-aging ingredient. Plus, the little black seeds are effective at exfoliating the skin. Mash the kiwifruit in a small bowl, then stir in the cornmeal. Massage into skin for a few minutes, then rinse.

A Toast to Smooth Skin

½ cup sugar
champagne

If you find yourself with some leftover champagne (we know, we know: Who would ever have leftover champagne?), try this super scrub. Measure out the sugar and add enough champagne to form a thick paste. Rub immediately into skin, then rinse with warm water.

Champagne contains tartaric acid, an enzyme that is a great natural exfoliant.

❋ BONUS BEAUTY TIP ❋

Want a quick way to exfoliate and moisturize at the same time? Try papaya. Mash a cup or two of papaya with a tablespoon or so of honey, and spread the mixture on the skin for five minutes. It can also help lighten blemishes and dark spots.

Chocolate-Honey Scrub

½ cup honey
½ cup sea salt
2 tablespoons cocoa powder
1 tablespoon olive oil

Who doesn't want to cover themselves in chocolate? Here's your opportunity with this hydrating, revitalizing scrub. Mix together all of the ingredients in a bowl, making sure to break up any lumps in the cocoa powder. Apply this luscious mixture to your skin, rubbing in a circular motion. Leave for five minutes, then rinse with warm water. Divine! (Leftover scrub can be stored in a tightly sealed container in the refrigerator.)

Strawberry Scrub

1 cup strawberries
2 tablespoons olive oil
2 tablespoons salt

This scrub is good for normal to dry skin, particularly for those flaky patches. Puree the strawberries and olive oil, then transfer to a small bowl. Stir in the salt. Use in the shower on damp skin, paying special attention to rough areas like the elbows and feet. Rinse with warm water.

Moisture-Minded

3 tablespoons baby oil
2 tablespoons yogurt
4 teaspoons brown sugar

Dry, itchy skin bothering you? Try this super-moisturizing light scrub. Mix together the ingredients, making sure to break up any lumps in the brown sugar. Massage immediately into skin, as the sugar will begin to dissolve. Rinse with warm water.

A Minty Morning

1 cup rice
6-ounce container plain yogurt
5 sprigs mint
3 drops peppermint essential oil

This invigorating scrub is great for those sleepy mornings when it's almost impossible to drag yourself out of
bed. For best results, make it the night before and store
in the refrigerator until morning. In a food processor, add
the rice and pulse until ground. Transfer the contents to
a bowl. Then process the yogurt and mint together and
add to the ground rice. Add the essential oil, stir well, and
refrigerate. Then, during your morning shower, rub the
mixture into your skin. You'll feel it working!

Cleansing Oat Scrub

½ cup quick oats
2 tablespoons sea salt
1–2 tablespoons milk

This simple scrub combines the cleansing power of oats with the exfoliating qualities of sea salt and milk. Stir together the oatmeal and sea salt and add enough milk to form a thick paste. Apply to damp skin using a circular motion, paying special attention to any rough spots. Rinse with warm water.

Ginger-Sugar Scrub

¾ cup raw sugar (turbinado or demerera)
¼ cup olive oil
1½ teaspoons grated fresh ginger

Ginger invigorates the skin, boosting circulation, while raw sugar rubs away any dry skin cells. Mix together all of the ingredients, making sure that the ginger is evenly distributed throughout. Rub on wet skin in the shower, then rinse clean.

✽ BONUS BEAUTY TIP ✽

We love this tip for chapped, winter skin. Place your regular lotion in a microwave-safe bowl, and microwave for 5–10 seconds. The warm lotion will feel great on cold mornings, and it will absorb faster into your skin than if it were at room temperature.

Use Your Veggies

2 ripe avocados
2 carrots, cooked
½ cup milk
2 eggs
¼ cup honey

This powerhouse of a body mask is loaded with vital nutrients to help rejuvenate and revitalize skin. To make it, mash together the avocados and carrots in a medium bowl. Stir in the milk, lightly beaten eggs, and honey. Apply the mixture to damp skin, then leave on for 10–15 minutes. Rinse with lukewarm water.

Anti-Inflammatory Body Mask

1 cup plain yogurt
1 teaspoon turmeric

Try this body mask to help soothe irritated skin. Combine the yogurt and the turmeric, blending well. Apply to damp skin, and leave for 10 minutes. Rinse with lukewarm water, then moisturize. The lactic acid in the yogurt gently breaks down dry skin cells, and turmeric is a well-known anti-inflammatory.

Strawberry Body Mask

1 cup strawberries, pureed
2 egg whites
2 teaspoons honey
1 teaspoon lemon juice

This body mask is great for summer, when strawberries are in season, and when skin tends to be a little oilier. Whisk the egg whites for a minute or two, then stir in the pureed strawberries. Add the honey and lemon juice and stir well. Apply to wet skin in the shower, and wait 15 minutes so that the enzymes in the fruit can work. Rinse with cool water. Your skin will feel tighter and smoother.

❋ BONUS BEAUTY TIP ❋

You were shaving too quickly, and now you have razor burn. Try some black tea! Soak a bag in water until it's plump, then squeeze out the excess. Apply directly to irritated skin. The tannins in tea help reduce inflammation.

Dry Skin Saver

2 tablespoons honey
2 tablespoons cocoa butter
3 drops essential oil (such as lavender or apricot)

Here's a great homemade moisturizer for dry skin that smells fantastic! Mix together all of the ingredients in a bowl. (You may need to microwave the cocoa butter for a few seconds to soften it.) Then apply the mixture to any particularly dry patches of skin.

Do you feel you're not really clean until your skin squeaks? You should know that you're stripping your skin of natural oils that keep it from drying out. Stick to non-detergent soaps and body cleansers.

Elbow Grease

2 tablespoons cornmeal or almond meal
2 tablespoons olive oil

For smooth elbows, try this moisturizing scrub. Mix the two ingredients together, and massage for a minute or two on rough elbows. The cornmeal will remove dry skin, while the olive oil will add moisture.

Wax On, Wax Off

1 cup white sugar
¼ cup honey
1 tablespoon lemon juice
body powder
cheesecloth or cotton strips

If you wax your legs, did you know that you can make your own sugar wax? In a saucepan, melt together all of the ingredients on low heat until they simmer and

start to darken. Remove from heat and allow to cool slightly. (This is an important step, because you don't want to burn yourself!) In the meantime, dust your legs with body powder. Then, using a brush, apply the warm sugar wax in the direction of the hair growth. Apply the cotton strip or cheesecloth in the same direction, press firmly, then pull off in the opposite direction.

Forget Facial Hair

1 tablespoon chickpea flour
1 teaspoon turmeric

To eliminate unwanted facial hair, try this unique trick. Mix together the chickpea flour (if you can't find it, you can grind dry chickpeas) with the turmeric. Add a little bit of water to make a paste, and apply to any spots where you have facial hair. Allow the paste to dry completely, then rub it off. Rinse the area with cool water.

❋ BONUS BEAUTY TIP ❋

Doing an at-home wax? For best results, make sure the hair is at least a quarter-inch long.

A Better Bustline

1 egg white
2 tablespoons plain yogurt
1 tablespoon honey
1 tablespoon grape-seed oil

Like the hands, the décolleté can be a big revealer of age. Turn back the clock—at least temporarily—with this firming mask. Whisk the egg white for a minute, then stir in the yogurt, honey, and oil. Brush on the chest, and wait 10–15 minutes. Rinse with warm water, and apply moisturizer.

Age Spots Solution

½ onion, grated
2 teaspoons white vinegar
1 tablespoon hydrogen peroxide

This one's a little stinky, but it sure helps with age spots and other blemishes. Take the grated onion, place it on a paper towel or cheesecloth, and squeeze out the onion juices in a small bowl. Mix in the vinegar and hydrogen peroxide. Dab a little onto unwanted spots each morning and evening.

Blotch Buster

¼ cup honey
2 tablespoons lemon juice
2 tablespoons sugar

Thanks to the lemon juice, this scrub has a gentle bleaching effect that's perfect for minor spots, blotches, and scars anywhere on the body. Mix the ingredients together and massage gently into the skin using a circular motion. Leave for 10 minutes, then rinse.

Pineapple Pore Toner

1 cup water
2 tablespoons fresh pineapple juice
1 vitamin C tablet

Use the enzymes in pineapple to help tone oily skin and reduce breakouts. Gently heat all of the ingredients in a saucepan on low until fully dissolved. Pour into a bottle and store in the refrigerator. Using a cotton ball, apply to clean skin. This is a great toner for the face, but also for other problem spots like the back.

❋ BONUS BEAUTY TIP ❋

For silky smooth legs, follow these two pre-shaving tips: Wait until you've been in the shower for at least five minutes, and then exfoliate your legs so that the razor can slide smoothly and grab each hair. Also, exfoliation helps prevent ingrown hairs.

Peppermint Tea Toner

1½ cups water
3 peppermint tea bags

Here's a great toner for oily skin, and it couldn't be simpler than just brewing up a really strong cup of peppermint tea! Bring the water to the boil in a small saucepan, and place the tea bags in it to steep for 20 minutes. Remove the bags, and transfer the tea to a bottle. You can store it in the refrigerator to make it last longer. Apply to clean, acne-prone skin.

Watermelon-Witch Hazel Wonder

1–2 slices watermelon
¼ cup witch hazel

Give the natural astringent witch hazel a boost with the power of watermelon. Juice one or two slices of watermelon; you want about ¼ cup juice. Add it to a bottle with the witch hazel and shake to combine. Use a cotton ball to apply to oily spots anywhere on the body. Store the leftovers in the refrigerator for up to a week.

✳ BONUS BEAUTY TIP ✳

For razor burn, try applying a liquid antacid. The active ingredient will calm redness and irritation. Rub some on the skin, leave for five minutes, then rinse.

CHAPTER 4

Going to Extremes: Pampering Your Hands and Feet

We all want well-manicured hands and feet, especially because they project an overall I've-got-it-together look (even if we don't really!). In this chapter, you'll find tons of great scrubs and other treatments that help eliminate unsightly calluses and rough skin, while also providing vital moisture. Also, you'll discover how to eliminate unpleasant odors, soothe aching feet, deal with nail problems, take years off aging hands, and tackle severely dry skin.

Summer-Ready Soles

½ cup Epsom salts
1 tablespoon petroleum jelly

Come spring, it's time to start thinking again about open-toed shoes. Slough the dry, rough patches off your feet with this great, basic foot scrub using two of the most common of household ingredients: Epsom salts and petroleum jelly. Mix the two together and, if you like, add a few drops of your favorite essential oil for a little fragrance. Use to scrub the soles of your feet, and soon they'll be sandal-worthy!

Strawberry Scrub

7–8 fresh strawberries
2 tablespoons olive oil
1 teaspoon coarse salt

Take advantage of the natural fruit acids in strawberries to make an effective scrub for the hands and feet. In a small bowl, mash the strawberries with a fork. Stir in the olive oil and salt. Rub onto hands and feet, rinse, and dry.

Odor Eater

¼ cup baking soda
5 drops essential oil (choose your favorite)

You know that baking soda is great for absorbing odors in your refrigerator, but did you know that you can also use it to keep your feet smelling sweet? On hot summer days, try this odor-busting foot powder. Mix together the baking soda and the essential oil, breaking up any lumps. Dust feet with the powder to reduce perspiration and odor. You can also sprinkle a little into stinky shoes.

Peppermint Powder

¼ cup unscented body powder
5 drops peppermint essential oil
5 drops tea tree oil

Keep your feet fresh and dry with this peppermint-scented foot powder. Place the ingredients in a Ziploc bag and seal carefully. You'll need to massage the

outside of the bag to get the oils to blend together evenly with the powder. To use, dust a little onto clean feet. The peppermint has a refreshing quality, and tea tree oil is a natural anti-fungal.

Peppermint Foot Scrub

1 cup sugar
2–3 tablespoons grape-seed (or other neutral) oil
5 drops peppermint essential oil

Some days it seems we never have a chance to sit down, and by the end of the day, our dogs are barking! Here's a great scrub that will both soothe and exfoliate those tired, aching feet. In a small bowl, add the sugar and begin drizzling in the oil until you have a coarse, damp mixture. Stir in the peppermint oil until well blended. Store in a Mason jar, and to use, rub a tablespoon or two onto the soles of your feet.

❃ BONUS BEAUTY TIP ❃

Let's face it: No one likes to talk about it, but foot fungus happens. Before you head to the doctor, give these simple home remedies a try. At night, apply some Vicks VapoRub to the affected area, and cover with socks while you sleep. You can also try soaking your feet in white vinegar once a day for a few days. If neither tip works, it's time to seek professional help.

DIY Foot Bath

Warm water
½ cup Epsom salts
5–10 drops essential oil (some ideas: eucalyptus,
    lavender, or peppermint)
marbles

For us, the best part of getting a pedicure is soaking
your feet in that warm bath at the salon. Here's an at-
home foot bath that's almost as good as the salon's!
Take a plastic basin and fill with warm to hot water (as
hot as you like). Stir in the Epsom salts and the essential
oil. Add a few handfuls of marbles to the bottom of the
basin. Stick your feet in the basin and relax, rubbing
your feet over the marbles for a gentle massage.

Moisturizing Foot Massage

Your favorite moisturizer
2 empty water bottles
2 washcloths

Here's another great home spa idea! Fill some water
bottles with warm water and cap tightly. Run the washcloths under warm water—as warm as is comfortable

for you. Apply the moisturizer to your feet and the warm washcloths on top of that. Then roll the warm water bottles under your feet.

❋ BONUS BEAUTY TIP ❋

Banish corns with an onion compress. Soak a dime-sized slice of onion in apple cider vinegar for a few hours. Remove it and place the onion over the corn, covering with a bandage. Put on cotton socks to protect the area and leave overnight. Repeat for a week for best results.

Refreshing Citrus Hand Scrub

¾ cup sugar
3 tablespoons coarse salt
½ cup olive (or grape-seed) oil
zest of a lemon or orange

This freshly scented hand (or foot) scrub gets a boost from citrus zest. In a medium bowl, mix together all of the ingredients, and pour into a resealable jar. Massage into your hands to help remove stains, food odors, or just for a simple exfoliation.

Citrusy Scrub

¼ cup freshly squeezed orange juice
2 tablespoons freshly squeezed lemon juice
½ cup sugar
1½ teaspoons apricot kernel oil

Here's another fruity scrub for the hands or feet. Squeeze the juice from the orange and lemon, straining out the pulp. Mix the juice with the sugar and apricot kernel oil to form a paste. Rub into calluses and other rough spots on your hands and feet, then rinse.

Fall Favorite

¼ cup applesauce
2 tablespoons brown sugar
1 tablespoon olive oil

We like to use this great-smelling hand scrub come autumn, when the air is just starting to get crisp and apples are in season. Mix together all of the ingredients in a small bowl. The brown sugar and acids in the apple juice offer a natural exfoliant, while the olive oil helps the skin retain moisture.

For Brighter Nails

1 lemon
baking soda

Before your next manicure, try this trick for whitening up nails that have been yellowed by polish. In a small bowl, squeeze the juice of a lemon, and add in enough baking soda so that you have a loose paste. Massage the mixture into your nails for a few minutes, then rinse.

❊ BONUS BEAUTY TIP ❊

Do you have dry nails? Garlic may be the answer. Add a little chopped garlic—no more than ⅛ teaspoon—to your bottle of clear base coat. Don't worry about the smell; the color and top coats will mask it entirely.

Sleight of Hand

1 tablespoon flaxseed oil
1 vitamin E capsule
cornmeal or ground flaxseed

Try this anti-aging scrub to help hide the truth! Mix together the flaxseed oil and vitamin E. Add enough cornmeal or ground flaxseed to make a coarse scrub. Massage gently into your hands, leave for five minutes, then rinse to reveal younger-looking hands.

Apricot Scrub

½ cup brown sugar
2 tablespoons lemon juice
2 tablespoons apricot kernel oil

Apricot kernel oil, available at vitamin and health-food stores, is rich in vitamins A and E and is an excellent moisturizer. Combine it with brown sugar and lemon juice for an exfoliating—and hydrating—hand scrub. Massage well into hands, then rinse.

❋ BONUS BEAUTY TIP ❋

Make sure to apply moisturizer to your hands and feet after you get out of the shower when the pores are still open.

Rosewater-Honey Rub

2 tablespoons rosewater
1 tablespoon honey
1 tablespoon apricot kernel oil
1 tablespoon lemon juice

For rough patches on the hands and feet, try this rub scented with rosewater, which has been used for centuries to soothe irritated skin and is thought to help regenerate skin tissue. Whisk together all of the ingredients in a small bowl. To use, rub onto rough patches on the hands and feet, then rinse.

Olive Oil Scrub

¼ cup olive oil
sugar

We love this olive oil scrub for its simplicity and effectiveness! In a small bowl, add the olive oil. Add enough sugar to make a damp, runny mixture. Rub it into your hands or feet, then rinse for smooth, moisturized skin.

Dry Rub

¼ cup flaxseed or almond meal
¼–½ teaspoon olive oil

In a small bowl, stir together the flaxseed or almond meal and olive oil. The mixture will be just barely damp. Rub well into dry, rough patches on your feet, then rinse.

Salty Solution

1 cup sea salt
olive oil

You can pay a lot of money for a fancy sea salt scrub, or you can make your very own version in just a few minutes. Sea salt contains natural minerals not present in regular table salt. It also helps remove dead skin cells and other toxins present in the skin. In a small bowl, add the sea salt and just enough olive oil to make a slightly runny mixture—you don't want it to be too loose. Rub into dry hands and feet for several minutes before rinsing off.

❉ BONUS BEAUTY TIP ❉

If you use a regular facial scrub in the shower, don't forget about your hands and feet. Use the same scrub to exfoliate them all at the same time!

A Spoonful of Sugar

1 tablespoon sugar
1 tablespoon sour cream

Try this quick hand scrub that combines the exfoliating power of sugar and the lactic acid in sour cream. Mix

the two ingredients together, and rub into hands for a minute or two. Rinse to reveal soft, smooth skin.

Buttermilk-Almond Hand Mask

½ cup buttermilk
1 tablespoon almond oil

Try this overnight hand mask to gently remove dead skin cells. Whisk together the buttermilk and almond oil in a small bowl. Submerge your hands completely, remove, and allow to dry. Then cover your hands with cotton gloves and leave on overnight. In the morning, rinse your hands well to reveal brighter skin.

Cucumber Foot Soak

2 cucumbers, peeled and chopped
2 tablespoons freshly squeezed lemon juice
2 tablespoons sweet almond oil

Try this cooling and moisturizing mask for sore feet. Puree the ingredients in the blender, then divide the puree into two large Ziploc bags. Place a foot in each bag and massage the mixture into your feet. Sit back and relax for 10–15 minutes. Remove your feet from the bags, then rinse well.

❋ BONUS BEAUTY TIP ❋

While you're watching television at night, give your cuticles a little love! Moisturize and massage them with hand cream.

Honey Hand Scrub

2 tablespoons honey
2 teaspoons lemon juice
½ cup sugar

This great-smelling scrub is perfect for removing dead skin cells from your hands! Whisk together the honey and lemon juice, then stir in the sugar. Rub into hands for a minute or two, then rinse and apply moisturizer.

Honey Hand Cream

¼ cup shortening, at room temperature
1 tablespoon honey
⅛ teaspoon rosewater

Come wintertime, combating severely dry skin can really seem like a losing battle. Whip up this intensive moisturizing cream to start fighting back. Stir together the shortening, honey, and rosewater in a bowl. Massage a little into those dry hands (or feet) anytime they need a little extra help. Store the leftovers in a tightly sealed jar.

  Who Knew? Beauty Wonders

Back to Basics

½ cup packed brown sugar
1 teaspoon olive oil

It doesn't get much simpler than this hand scrub. Mix together the sugar and olive oil until well blended. Gently massage into hands or feet to exfoliate, then rinse. Follow with your regular moisturizer.

Oatmeal and Brown Sugar Foot Mask

¼ cup packed brown sugar
¼ cup rolled oats
¼ cup honey
1 tablespoon lemon juice
1 tablespoon olive oil

This foot mask is almost good enough to eat! In a food processor, pulse together the oatmeal and brown sugar. Transfer to a small bowl and stir in the honey, lemon juice, and olive oil. Divide the mixture into two Ziploc bags, and place your feet in the bags. Massage the paste into the feet, and leave for 10 minutes. Rinse with warm water.

CHAPTER 5

Baths, Butters, Lotions, and More

In our opinion, we've saved the best for last. In this chapter, you'll learn how to create a luxurious spa experience right at home, using all-natural ingredients. Try a deep moisturizing body butter, like our chocolate body butter. Ease aches and pains with chamomile-lavender bath salts, or calm irritated skin with the cinnamon-oatmeal soak. Make your own fizzy bath bombs. Bathe amidst rose petals. Many of these recipes make great gifts, too; just put the product in a fancy jar and decorate!

Basic Body Butter

6 tablespoons shea butter
3 tablespoons cocoa butter
3 tablespoons apricot kernel oil

To start things off, here's a basic yet effective body butter. If you want to add additional fragrance, include a few drops of your favorite essential oil. In a small saucepan, add the cocoa butter, shea butter, and oil. On low heat, allow the butters to melt together, stirring regularly. As soon as they're melted, remove from the heat and whisk thoroughly. Pour the mixture into a cosmetics jar and allow it to cool completely. A little goes a long way!

Coconut-Almond Butter

½ cup shea butter
¼ cup coconut oil
¼ cup sweet almond oil

In a double boiler on low heat, melt the shea butter and coconut oil together, stirring regularly. Allow to cool before stirring in the almond oil. Using a hand mixer or sturdy whisk, whip the mixture together. Transfer to a cosmetics jar or other storage container.

Nuts for Coconut!

1 cup coconut oil
your favorite essential oil

Frankly, this coconut butter couldn't be simpler, and yet it's so luxurious! Place the coconut oil in a bowl, and using a hand mixer, blend it until it's the consistency of whipped butter. Add five drops of your favorite essential oil, and continue mixing until evenly combined. Transfer the mixture to a glass jar, and it's ready to use anytime your skin needs a little extra help.

❋ BONUS BEAUTY TIP ❋

Having a hard time waking up in the morning? Try Altoids—but not in your mouth. Place one on the floor of your shower, and as you bathe, it will dissolve, releasing a stimulating scent.

Chocolate Body Butter

1 cup coconut oil
¼ cup cocoa powder
¼ teaspoon vanilla powder
1 vitamin E capsule

What could be more decadent than chocolate body butter? Chocolate contains antioxidants that give skin a firmer, more youthful look. Place all of the ingredients in a bowl, squeezing out the contents of the vitamin E capsule. With a hand mixer, begin to beat on low. As the cocoa becomes incorporated, increase the speed until the mixture is the texture of whipped butter. Transfer to an airtight container, and store in a cool, dry place.

After Burn

¼ cup aloe vera gel
2 tablespoons filtered water
3 drops peppermint oil

Give regular aloe vera gel a little boost with soothing peppermint. Use this lotion on sunburned or dry skin. In a small bowl, combine the aloe vera and water. Microwave on low, stirring regularly, until they are well

combined. Stir in the peppermint oil, and allow to cool. Place the mixture in a cosmetics jar. Massage into skin for a few minutes, and rinse if desired. The aloe will have a cooling effect, and the peppermint will provide a little relaxing tingle.

❋ BONUS BEAUTY TIP ❋

To help ease sunburn, add a half-cup of baking soda to luke-warm bathwater.

Honey-Lavender Bath

2 tablespoons dried lavender
1 cup milk
¼ cup honey
3 drops lavender essential oil (optional)

Good for soothing dry skin and relieving stress, this honey-lavender bath is quick and easy to make. Process the lavender in a food processor until it becomes a powder, and transfer it to a small bowl. Whisk in the milk, honey, and essential oil until well combined. Pour the mixture into a hot bath, relax, and enjoy!

Go-To Milk Bath

3 cups powdered milk
¼ cup oatmeal
¼ cup almond meal
¼ cup cornstarch

The great thing about this milk bath is that you can make a large quantity of it all at once, and then store the rest for multiple uses. In a food processor, pulse the oatmeal until it is powdery. Pour all of the ingredients into a large Ziploc bag, seal, and shake to combine thoroughly. When you want to use it, measure out a ½ cup into a cheesecloth or sachet, and tie it closed. Add to your hot bathwater. For an extra-moisturizing bath, break open a vitamin E capsule and add to the water.

✳ BONUS BEAUTY TIP ✳

If you suffer from dry skin, don't soak in an overheated bath. The hot water can dry out the skin even further. Use warm water instead, and moisturize well afterward.

Da Bomb Bath Fizzies

1 cup citric acid powder
1 cup baking soda
½ cup cornstarch
½ cup grape-seed oil
10 drops essential oil (choose your favorite)
5 drops food coloring (optional)
cookie cutters, silicone molds, or ice cube trays

You've seen those fancy bath bombs in bath and body stores, right? Did you know you can easily make your own? You do need one hard-to-find ingredient, citric acid powder, which you can locate online or at some supermarkets in the canning section. (It's what reacts with the baking soda to make that fizzy sound—kind of like those baking soda and vinegar volcanoes you'd make as a child.) This is a great winter craft because the bath bombs set up best on low-humidity days. Mix together the citric acid, baking soda, cornstarch, and oil until you have a crumbly dough. Stir in the essential oil of your choice and the optional food coloring. Press the mixture firmly into the molds or ice cube trays, and then let dry for 24 hours. Remove carefully. Depending on the size of the bomb, you can use one or two per bath.

Simple Bath Salts

1 cup Epsom salts
¼ cup baking soda
¼ cup powdered milk
¼ cup cornstarch
your favorite essential oil

To relax sore muscles and soften skin, try these basic bath salts. Mix together the Epsom salts, baking soda, powdered milk, and cornstarch in a small bowl. Add this to a warm bath along with a few drops of your favorite essential oil.

❋ BONUS BEAUTY TIP ❋

To ease aching muscles, try a little mustard! Add a few tablespoons dry mustard powder to your bath. It will help enhance circulation and offer some pain relief.

Vanilla-Cinammon Salts

1 cup Epsom salts
1 teaspoon cinnamon
¼ teaspoon vanilla extract

Perfect for aches and pains, these bath salts smell like warm cookies once they hit the water! Mix together the Epsom salts, cinnamon, and vanilla extract, then pour into running bathwater.

Chamomile-Lavender Salt Bath

1 cup Epsom salts
½ cup chamomile
¼ cup lavender

Place the chamomile and lavender in a small sachet or cheesecloth, and tie it closed. Add the Epsom salts to hot running water, and toss the herbal sachet into the tub. You'll have a fragrant, stress-relieving soak, and the magnesium in the Epsom salts will alleviate muscle pain.

Milky Tea Bath

2 cups milk
4 bags peppermint tea

This bath combines the revitalizing qualities of peppermint, along with the soothing and exfoliating properties of milk. Heat the milk until warm, and add the tea bags. Allow to steep for 20 minutes before removing the bags. Add this mixture to your bath.

❋ BONUS BEAUTY TIP ❋

Now you finally have a use for those foam peanuts used as packing materials: a bath pillow! Place the packing peanuts in a Ziploc bag and seal tightly, making sure to release any air. You'll have a comfortable way of propping up your head while you relax in the tub.

Pampering Honey-Sea Salt Bath

2 cups milk
¾ cup honey
½ cup sea salt

In this luxurious bath, milk and salt provide gentle exfoliation, while the honey moisturizes. In a small saucepan over medium heat, heat the milk, honey, and sea salt until dissolved. Cool slightly, and add this mixture to your bathwater, swirling to combine.

DIY Rose Lotion

1 cup sweet almond oil
1 ounce beeswax
½ cup rosewater
2 drops rose essential oil

We love this rose lotion, which has such a classic scent. In a double boiler, melt together the beeswax and sweet almond oil, stirring constantly. Remove from the heat, and transfer to a bowl. Whisk in the rosewater and essential oil, and allow to cool. Beat thoroughly to recombine, and transfer to a clean, airtight container.

Rinse-Off Chamomile Body Lotion

1 cup dried chamomile (available online at Amazon.com)
1¼ cups milk
¼ cup honey
2 tablespoons olive oil

For smooth, moisturized skin, try rubbing on this lotion before bathing. In a bowl, allow the chamomile to steep in the milk for a few hours. Strain, discarding the chamomile. Whisk the honey and oil into the richly infused milk. Right before you shower, massage the mixture all over your body and leave for 5–10 minutes. Then rinse with warm water and shower as usual.

Make your bath a special time: Turn off your phone. The fewer distractions you have, the more relaxing the experience will be.

Strawberry Lotion

2 tablespoons olive oil

1 tablespoon coconut oil

3–4 strawberries

1 vitamin E capsule

Here's another rinse-off lotion that's ideal for severely dry skin. Puree the strawberries in a blender with the olive oil, coconut oil, and the contents of a vitamin E capsule. Smooth onto skin before showering, leave on for 5–10 minutes, then rinse with warm water.

Ginger Face and Body Polish

¼ cup coconut oil

2 tablespoons fresh ginger, chopped

¼ cup olive oil

¾ cup raw sugar

¼ cup sea salt

For beach-ready skin, try this body polish. Ginger will help stimulate the skin, salt and sugar will rub away dead skin cells, and the combination of coconut and olive oils will provide deep hydration. In a small saucepan, add the coconut oil and grated ginger, and heat on low until the oil melts and the ginger has infused it. Strain into a bowl. Stir in the olive oil, sugar, and sea salt, and allow the mixture to cool. Transfer to a cosmetics jar. To use, massage a little into the face and body, and leave for five minutes before rinsing under warm water.

Salty Lemon Scrub

1 cup sea salt
3–4 tablespoons olive oil
1 teaspoon lemon juice
zest of one lemon

This simple salt scrub uses ingredients almost everyone already has around the house. In a small bowl, add the sea salt, and begin drizzling in the olive oil until you have a damp mixture. Stir in the lemon juice and zest, and put the scrub in an airtight storage container. To use, massage into damp skin, then rinse with warm water.

A Spoonful of Sugar

½ cup packed brown sugar
2 tablespoons ground coffee
2 tablespoons olive oil
1 tablespoon honey
1 vitamin E capsule

To reduce the appearance of cellulite while exfoliating, try this brown sugar and coffee scrub. In a small bowl, mix together all of the ingredients. Massage a small amount on damp, clean skin for a few minutes, using circular motions. Rinse with warm water.

❊ BONUS BEAUTY TIP ❊

Craving a bubble bath, but don't have the proper products on hand? Try grating castile soap into warm water and stirring to combine. To add fragrance, put in a drop or two of essential oil.

Almond Bubble Bath

1 cup unscented liquid castile soap (such as Dr. Bronner's)
2 tablespoons honey
½ teaspoon almond extract

For special bath, here are some super-simple bath suds. Mix together the liquid soap, honey, and almond extract in a resealable container. To use, place a tablespoon or two under hot running water.

Bubble Bath Gels

1 envelope unflavored gelatin
¾ cup water
½ cup unscented liquid soap (such as Dr. Bronner's)
your favorite essential oil
food coloring (optional)

We love these incredible bath gels! Make some for yourself or give them out as gifts. (During the holidays, try scenting them with seasonal oils for a special treat.)

In a small bowl, pour in the gelatin. Bring the water to a boil and pour over the gelatin, stirring until it's fully dissolved. Then stir in the soap and a few drops of the essential oil of your choice. For an extra twist, add a drop or two of food coloring. Pour the mixture into a storage container and refrigerate until the mixture is set. To use, place a tablespoon or so of the gel under running bathwater.

Take advantage of the many skin benefits of green tea with this simple bath. Just toss in a few tea bags when you start to run the water.

Humectant Honey Bath

½ cup grape-seed oil
¼ cup honey
¼ cup liquid castile soap (such as Dr. Bronner's)

For dry, irritated skin, try this moisturizing honey bubble bath. Mix together the oil, honey, and soap, being careful not to froth them up too much. Then pour the mixture into a squeeze bottle. You may need to shake it up before using. Add a few tablespoons under running bathwater. The leftovers will store well in a cool, dry place.

Soothing Cinammon-Oatmeal Soak

1/3 cup oatmeal
¾ cup powdered milk
1/3 cup baking soda
2 tablespoons cornstarch
2 teaspoons cinnamon

For soft, smooth skin, try this cinnamon-oatmeal soak. In a food processor, pulse the oatmeal until it's a fine powder. Transfer it to a small bowl, and stir in the powdered milk, baking soda, cornstarch, and cinnamon, making sure to break up any lumps. Place in a cheesecloth and tie to secure. Add the sachet to hot bathwater.

Peppy Peppermint Bath

1 cup warm water
½ cup powdered milk
¼ cup cornstarch
5 drops peppermint essential oil

This peppermint bath is sure to stimulate your senses and get your skin tingling! Add the powdered milk and cornstarch to the warm water, and whisk until thoroughly combined. Stir in the essential oil, and pour the entire mixture into your bathwater.

❃ BONUS BEAUTY TIP ❃

Don't have time to mix up any of these concoctions? Just add two tablespoons of sea salt and a few drops of essential oil to any bath for a special treat.